Soon—

NO, DENNIS! YOU'RE NOT GOING TO GO SWIMMING WITH THOSE CROCODILES, ARE YOU? BUT YOU'RE TOO ROUGH!

OOOHHHH!

NOBE. JUS' PUDDIN' ONNA NODE CLIP TO SHOW YOU 'OW A SKUNK PROTECTS ITSELF.

WIGGLE!

CHEEKY MENACE!

I'LL GIVE OFF A BLAST OF GUFF!

PONG!

PAF!

THAT'S HOW A SKUNK PROTECTS ITSELF!

PACKS QUITE A PUNCH!

MUNCH! SCOFF!

Pie Face's lunch

AND THE GIANT TORTOISE HIDES INSIDE HIS SHELL TO PROTECT HIMSELF!

ZIP!

ZIP!

SO I'LL LET YOU SOFT BOYS HIDE INSIDE THIS SHELL TO PROTECT YOU! HAR-HAR!

Pie Face's lunch

WHIMPERS!!!!

HELP! WE'RE TRAPPED!

AND IT'S DARK IN HERE!

Pie Face's lunch

AND PIE GRAVY HAS DRIPPED ALL OVER MY NEW SHIRT! RUINED, IT IS!

HUMPH! TIME TO PROTECT EVERYBODY AND EVERY ANIMAL AT THE ZOO, I THINK!

HUH?

GNUH?

DO NOT FEED THE ANIMALS

THERE! NOW WE CAN ENJOY THE SCHOOL TRIP IN PEACE AND SAFETY!

OO! LOOK! A COUPLE OF WILD MENACES!

HAIR BRAINS!

TIME TO WASH MY CAR. IT'S RATHER MUCKY.
JET WASH
BETTER STILL, I'LL WASH THOSE MENACES' HAIR FOR THEM! IT'S ALL THICK AND STICKY AS USUAL!
GLARRGGHH!!!!
GNASTY!!!!!

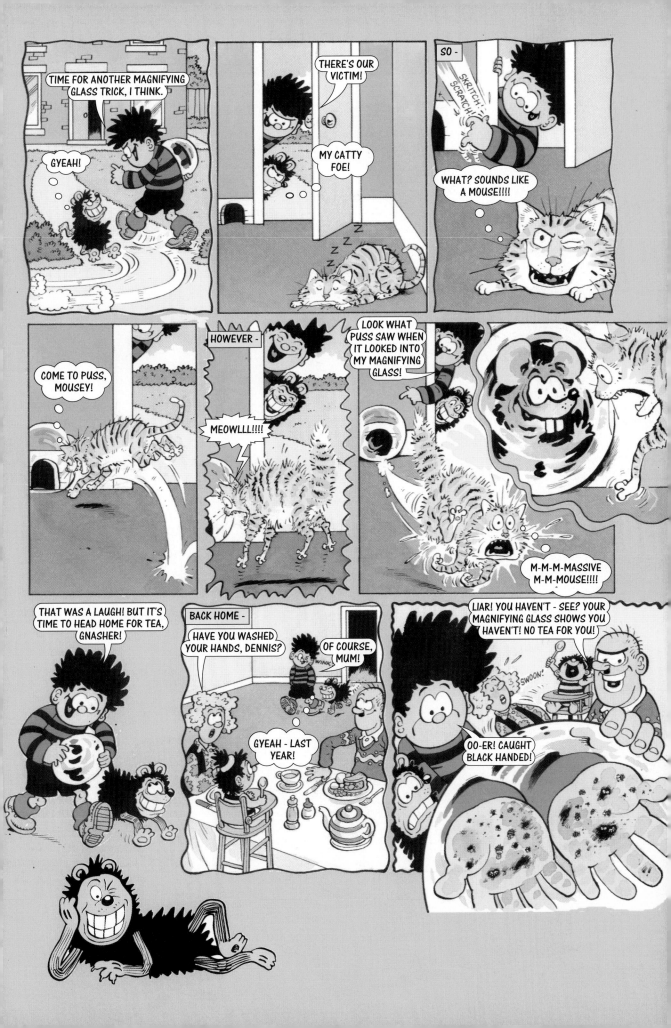

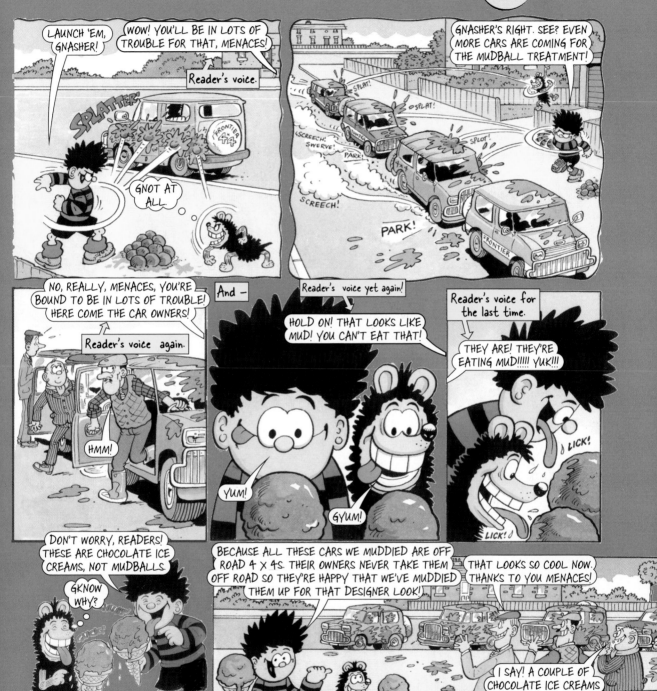

LAUNCH 'EM, GNASHER!

WOW! YOU'LL BE IN LOTS OF TROUBLE FOR THAT, MENACES!

Reader's voice.

SPLATTER!

GNOT AT ALL.

GNASHER'S RIGHT. SEE? EVEN MORE CARS ARE COMING FOR THE MUDBALL TREATMENT!

SPLAT!

OSPLAT!

SCREECH! SWERVE!

PARK!

SPLOT!

SCREECH!

PARK!

FRONTIER

NO, REALLY, MENACES, YOU'RE BOUND TO BE IN LOTS OF TROUBLE! HERE COME THE CAR OWNERS!

And -

Reader's voice yet again!

Reader's voice again.

HMM!

HOLD ON! THAT LOOKS LIKE MUD! YOU CAN'T EAT THAT!

YUM!

GYUM!

Reader's voice for the last time.

THEY ARE! THEY'RE EATING MUD!!!!! YUK!!!

LICK!

LICK!

DON'T WORRY, READERS! THESE ARE CHOCOLATE ICE CREAMS, NOT MUDBALLS.

GKNOW WHY?

BECAUSE ALL THESE CARS WE MUDDIED ARE OFF ROAD 4 x 4S. THEIR OWNERS NEVER TAKE THEM OFF ROAD SO THEY'RE HAPPY THAT WE'VE MUDDIED THEM UP FOR THAT DESIGNER LOOK!

THAT LOOKS SO COOL NOW. THANKS TO YOU MENACES!

I SAY! A COUPLE OF CHOCOLATE ICE CREAMS FOR YOU TWO GUYS!

MENACING
CATS and DOGS

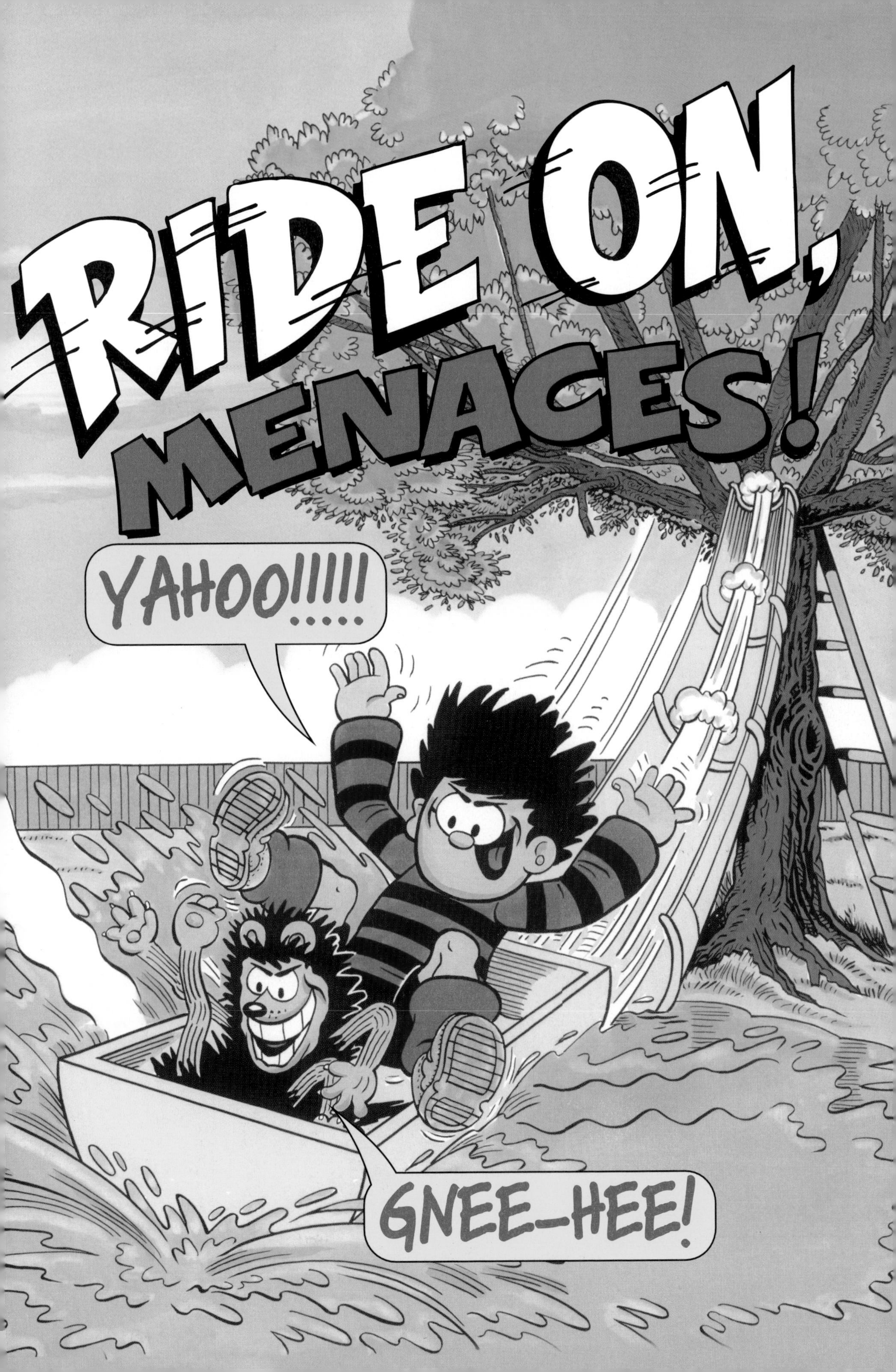
RIDE ON, MENACES!
YAHOO!!!!!!.....
GNEE-HEE!

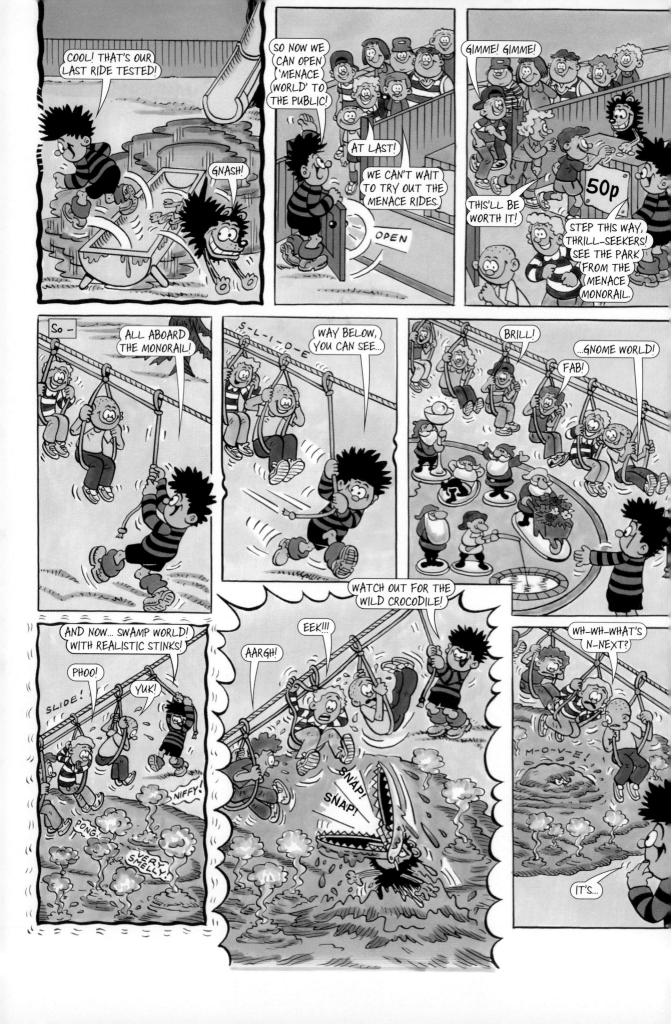

IF THIS WAS MY ANN

...I'D ADD SOME PENSIONER POWER!

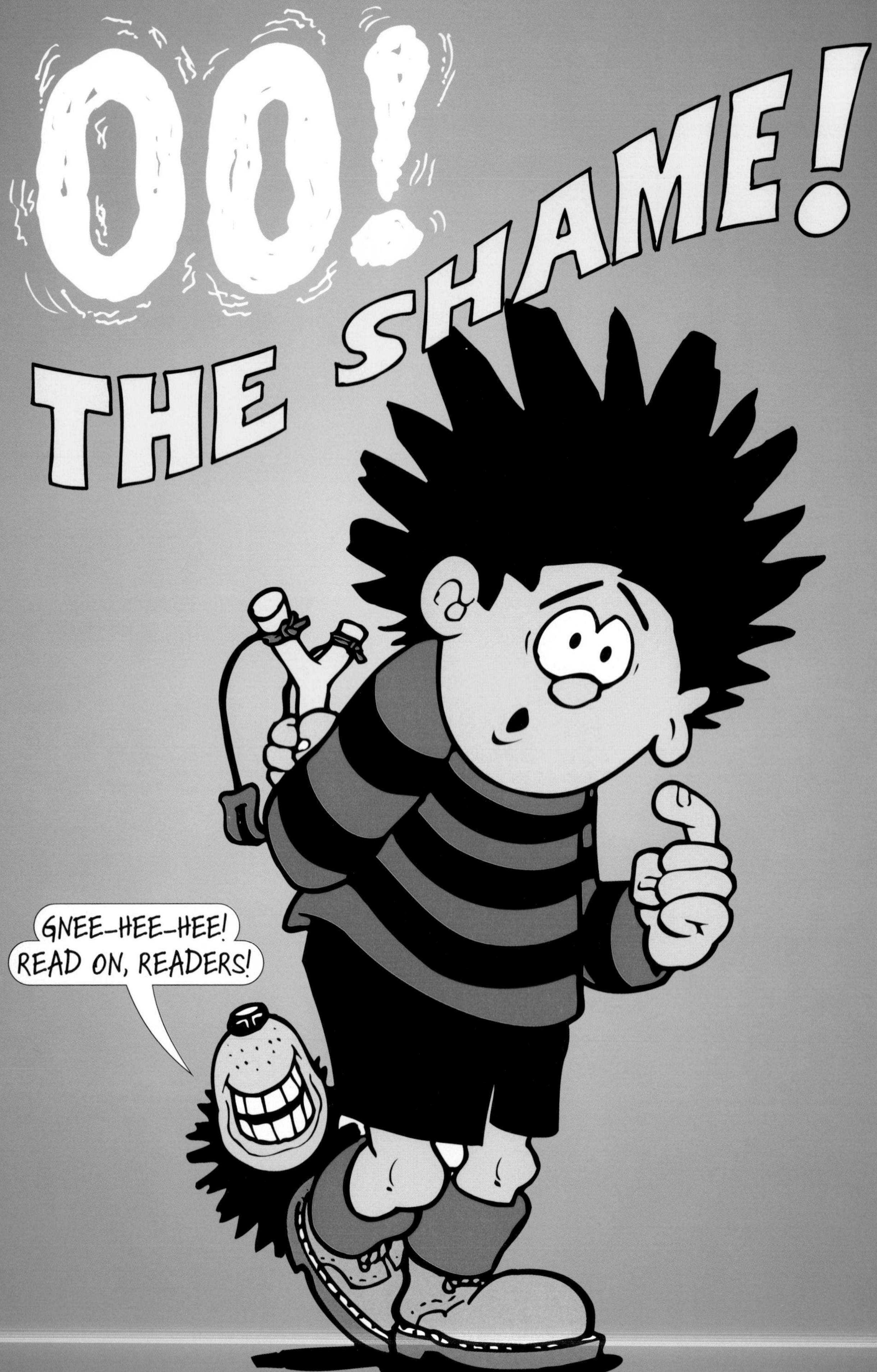
OO! THE SHAME!
GNEE-HEE-HEE! READ ON, READERS!

Soon –

ROGER THE DODGER! AND PLUG! OUR NEXT VICTIMS!

HERE WE COME, ROGER!

ZOOM!

SWERVE!

HEH-HEH! THEY DON'T CALL ME A DODGER FOR NOTHING!

WH–? WHERE'D HE GO? WHY ARE WE FLYING?

DODGEMS

CRASH!

VROOM!

MISSED! PITY, I WANTED TO MAKE A COCONUT PIE!

TOK!

NO CHANCE! I'VE GLUED THE NUTS!

GLUE

So –

CRASH!

HAVE ALL THE NUTS, PIE-FACE!

TA, DENNIS!

PITY WE CAN'T STOP!

TUNNEL OF LOVE

GNULP! THE TUNNEL OF LOVE!

KISSY-WISSY!

HONEY-BUN!

OH, NO! I'VE ALREADY HAD A BATH THIS YEAR!

SPLASH!

SMOOCHY-WOOCHY!

OO! TELL ME THIS ISN'T HAPPENING!

TITTER! A LOVELY SNAP TO SHOW MY SOFTY CHUMS!

HA-HA!

TIME US MENACES RE-TYRED!

DENNIS the MENACE in THE 12 DAYS OF MENACING

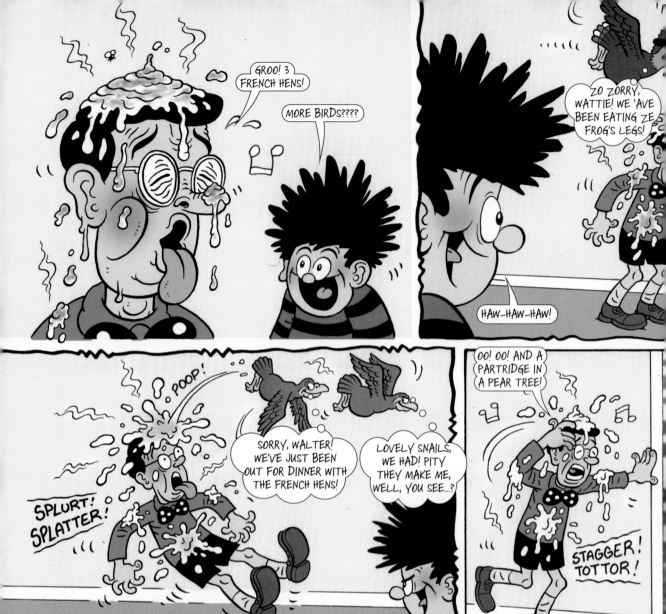